DOLL DILEMMA

When Sergei came from Russia to visit his friends, he brought along a traditional doll. But Sergei dropped the doll and it came apart. To put all the dolls back correctly, each of the smaller ones will fit inside the next largest doll until only one is left. Can you list the dolls in order from the smallest to the largest, so Sergei can put them all back together?

Answer on page 47.

Illustrated by Terry Rogers

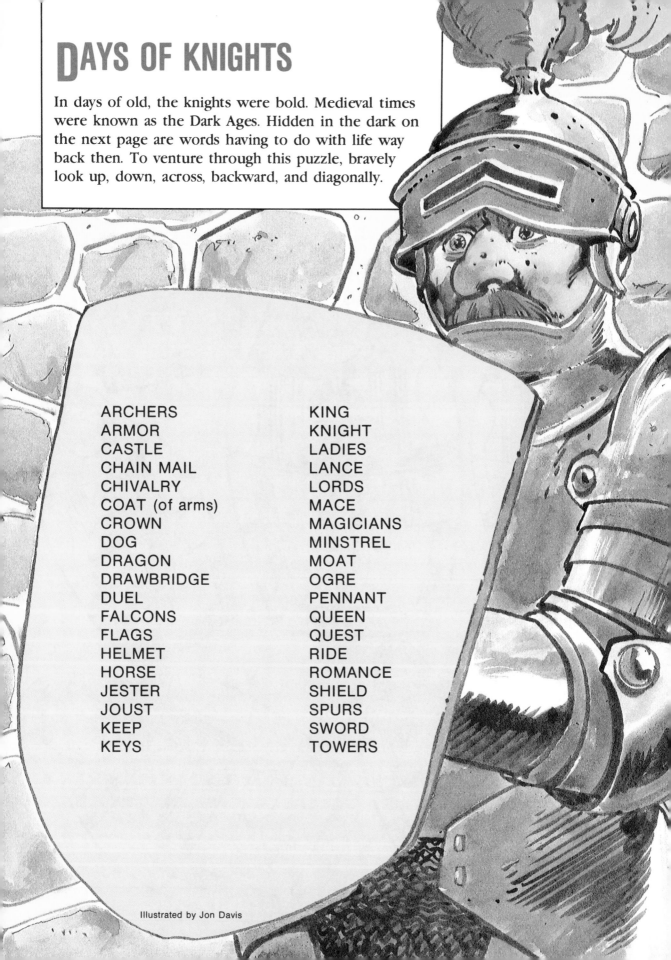

DAYS OF KNIGHTS

In days of old, the knights were bold. Medieval times were known as the Dark Ages. Hidden in the dark on the next page are words having to do with life way back then. To venture through this puzzle, bravely look up, down, across, backward, and diagonally.

ARCHERS
ARMOR
CASTLE
CHAIN MAIL
CHIVALRY
COAT (of arms)
CROWN
DOG
DRAGON
DRAWBRIDGE
DUEL
FALCONS
FLAGS
HELMET
HORSE
JESTER
JOUST
KEEP
KEYS

KING
KNIGHT
LADIES
LANCE
LORDS
MACE
MAGICIANS
MINSTREL
MOAT
OGRE
PENNANT
QUEEN
QUEST
RIDE
ROMANCE
SHIELD
SPURS
SWORD
TOWERS

Illustrated by Jon Davis

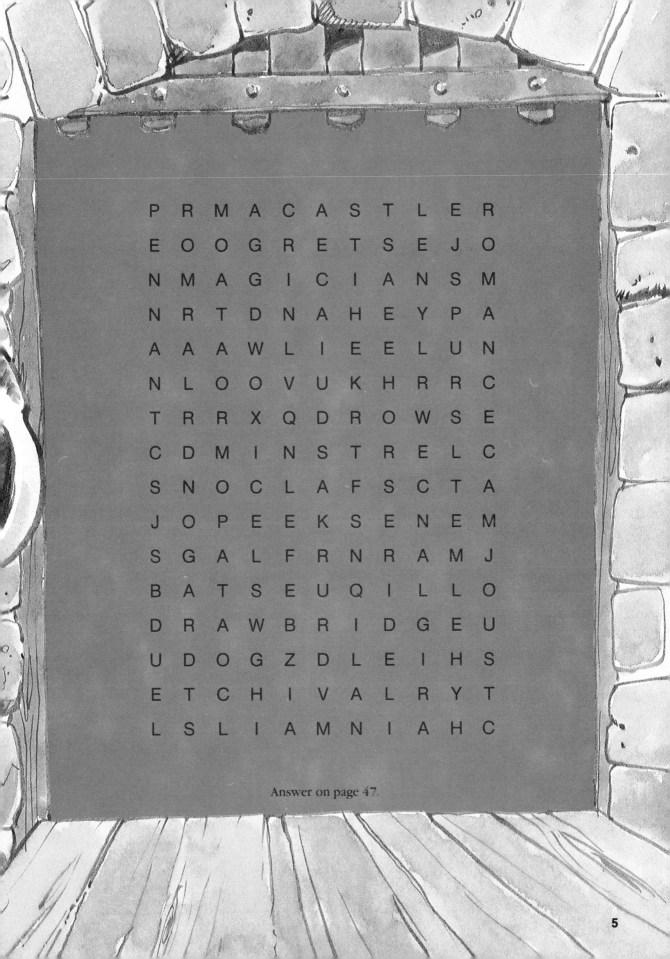

```
P R M A C A S T L E R
E O O G R E T S E J O
N M A G I C I A N S M
N R T D N A H E Y P A
A A A W L I E E L U N
N L O O V U K H R R C
T R R X Q D R O W S E
C D M I N S T R E L C
S N O C L A F S C T A
J O P E E K S E N E M
S G A L F R N R A M J
B A T S E U Q I L L O
D R A W B R I D G E U
U D O G Z D L E I H S
E T C H I V A L R Y T
L S L I A M N I A H C
```

Answer on page 47.

CHECK OUT THAT SHAPE

Gordon went grocery shopping for the family. Look at the shapes of the items on the checkout counter, and try to match each one with the items on his list. Write the numbers from the list on each shape to help Gordon figure out if he got everything he needed.

1. Celery
2. Box of cereal
3. Apple
4. Carrot
5. Grapes
6. Loaf of bread
7. Can of soup
8. Pear
9. Mustard
10. One dozen eggs
11. Box of cookies
12. Box of oatmeal
13. Bananas
14. Bottle of catsup
15. Four-roll package of toilet paper
16. Carton of milk

Answer on page 47.

FOREIGN PHRASES

The numbers 1 through 10 appear below in both Spanish and English. Use the size of each word to figure out where it fits in the squares. Both the first "ones" have been done to get you started. The way to pronounce each Spanish word is in parenthesis.

ENGLISH	SPANISH
ONE	UNO (oo-no)
TWO	DOS (dose)
THREE	TRES (trays)
FOUR	CUATRO (kwa-tro)
FIVE	CINCO (sinko)
SIX	SEIS (says)
SEVEN	SIETE (see-et-ay)
EIGHT	OCHO (o-cho)
NINE	NUEVE (new-a-vay)
TEN	DIEZ (dee-aze)

O N E
U N O

Answer on page 47.

Illustrated by John Nez

FAST FLOYD'S FLOWERS

Floyd the florist needs to make some fast deliveries. He has to stop at the dentist, music store, bank, apartment building, church, the department store, and the library. He has been instructed to use only the front door of each building. Without going in reverse, can you help Floyd find the shortest driving route around town and back to his shop?

Illustrated by John Nez

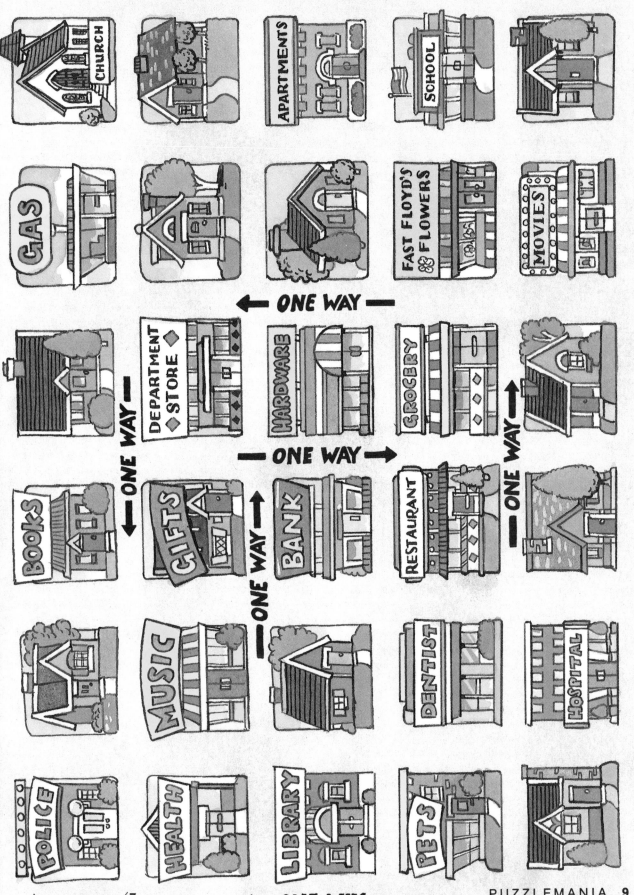

STRANGE SEQUENCES

Each list of letters is a sequence of some kind. Can you figure out what each sequence is and what letter will go in the blank? The first sequence should be a snap, but be careful. The others are tricky.

1. A B C D E F G ___

2. J F M A M J J ___

3. S M T W T F ___

4. R O Y G B ___

5. C D E F G A ___

6. O T T F F S ___

7. M V E M J S U N ___

8. T F S E T T ___

Illustrated by Gregg Valley

Answer on page 48.

INSTANT PICTURE

To discover a great wintertime friend, fill in each space that has two dots.

Illustrated by Rob Sepanak

Answer on page 48.

DEEP SLEEP

Professor Hink Pink is in a deep sleep. As is his style, he's having a strange range of dreams. For example, in this one there are lots of animals moving by him on land, in the water, or in the air. Of course, all the animals and their vehicles rhyme, like a duck truck. Without waking the Professor, can you find the other rhymes in his dream scene?

Answer on page 48.

Illustrated by Terry Rogers

M IS FOR MONSTERS

There are at least 30 objects in this picture that begin with the letter "M."
How many can you find?

FISHING LINE

Cross off all the pairs of letters in the same line until you find the one that has no match. Put that letter in the box with the number that matches each line. When you're done, you'll have the answer to the riddle below.

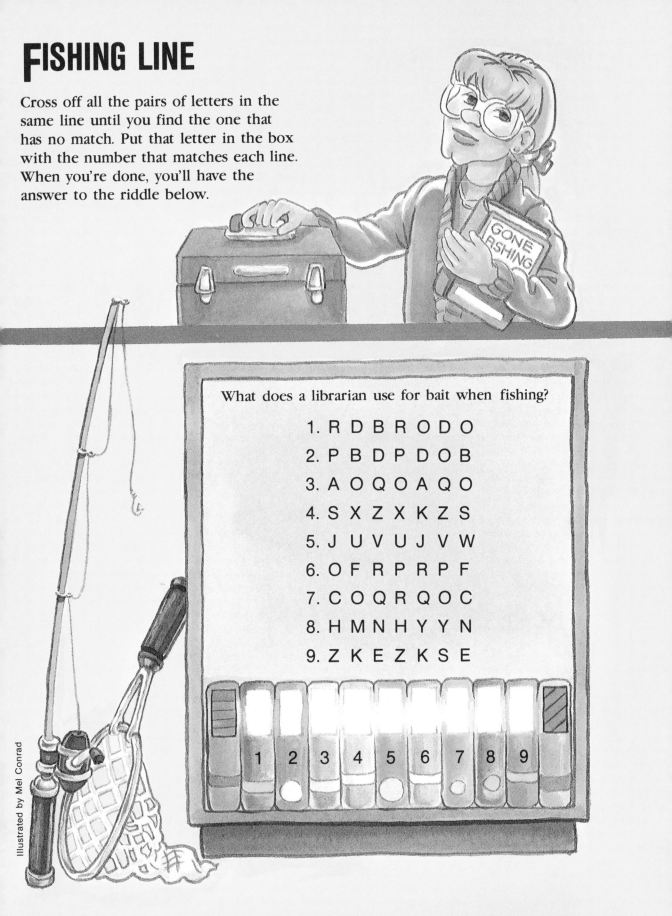

What does a librarian use for bait when fishing?

1. R D B R O D O
2. P B D P D O B
3. A O Q O A Q O
4. S X Z X K Z S
5. J U V U J V W
6. O F R P R P F
7. C O Q R Q O C
8. H M N H Y Y N
9. Z K E Z K S E

1 2 3 4 5 6 7 8 9

Illustrated by Mel Conrad

ROME, SWEET ROME

Can you use your knowledge of Roman numerals to complete this crossnumber puzzle? Fill in the grid as if it were a regular crossword, substituting numbers for letters. When the clue is in Roman numerals, you should write in the equivalent number in regular Arabic numerals. When the clue is an Arabic numeral, write in the Roman numerals. The chart will give you some help in remembering the Roman numbers.

M = 1,000	X = 10
D = 500	V = 5
C = 100	I = 1
L = 50	

Also remember, in Roman numerals, when a letter of a smaller number is placed before the letter of a larger number, the smaller number is meant to be subtracted. Example: CD = 500 - 100 and so the answer will be 400.

ACROSS

1. MMCDLXVIII
4. MCCCLII
8. DCCIII
10. DCXL
11. XVI
12. 1,200
14. XCV
15. 3,105
17. 762
19. 616
21. XXI
23. 12
24. LVI
25. DCCCIX
27. CLXXIX
28. MMCCXXXIV
29. MDCIII

DOWN

1. MMDCCXV
2. CDVI
3. LXIII
5. XXXVI
6. DXLIX
7. MML
9. 1,969
12. 2,210
13. 216
15. 1,400
16. 7
18. MMMCCLXXXII
20. MMMDCXCIII
22. CII
24. DLXX
26. XCIII
27. XVI

ROW, ROW, ROW

Looking down from your window on a very rainy day, you might see all these umbrellas waiting for the bus. Each umbrella has something in common with the two others in the same row. For example, in the top row across, each umbrella has a blue background. Look at the other rows across, down, and diagonally. What's the same about each row of three?

Answer on page 48.

LUCKY LIST

You'll be lucky if you can unscramble these words. All the items below are superstitions, considered to bring either good luck or bad luck.

DOGO

ORUF-EFAL VERLOC
BOSHNEWI
BITBAR'S TOOF
FECA-PU NYNEP
ROSHESOHSE
GHOSTINO RATS

ABD

PETSPING NO WALEDISK SCARCK
NEPO LUMBERLA DESINI
KLAW DENRU DERDAL
CACKERD RIMROR
CLAKB STAC
PILESLD LAST

Answer on page 48.

WEATHER WORRIES

May Merryweather is a magnificent meteorologist. She uses a lot of different information to find out what the weather will be. Her Aunt Augusta constantly calls for information on what weather other family members are enjoying. Using the two information keys above her map, see if you can help May answer all of Aunt Augusta's questions.

1. "Your niece, Natalie, is navigating the Great Lakes. What's the temperature and weather like around the lakes today?"

2. "Who's warmer—Aunt Minnie in Ohio or Cousin Vinnie in Oklahoma?"

3. "Cousin Gladys was suppose to fly to Maine. But now they say the airport is closed. Why is that?"

4. "My brother Barry went to see Cecil in Seattle, Washington. What's the weather and temperature there?"

5. "Aunt Mona's gone to Arizona. What's the temperature range there today?"

6. "What's the weather and temperature for Flo in southern Florida?"

7. "People keep calling to bother me, so I need to get away. Where's the warmest spot in the country?"

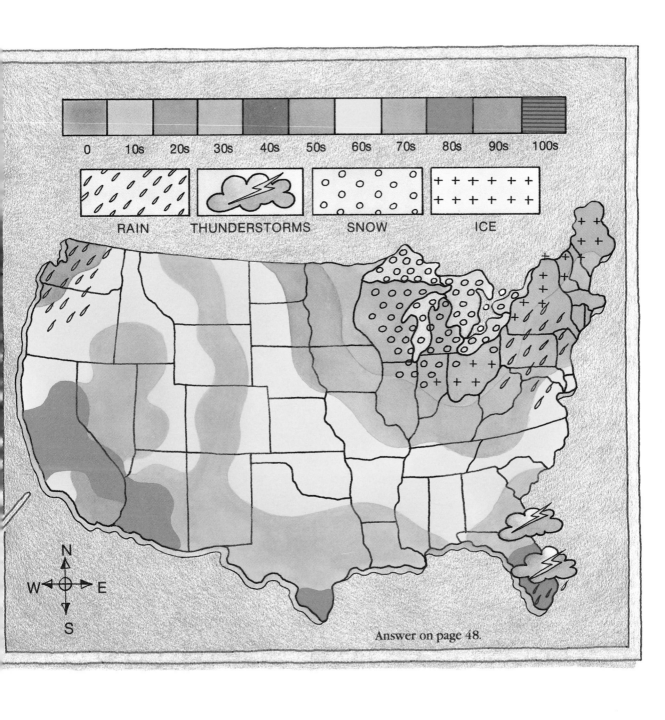

0 10s 20s 30s 40s 50s 60s 70s 80s 90s 100s

RAIN   THUNDERSTORMS   SNOW   ICE

N
W ⊕ E
S

Answer on page 48.

Illustrated by Barbara Gray

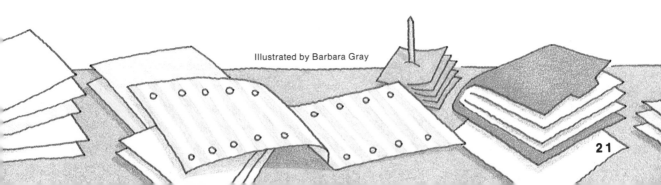

PICTURE MIXER

Copy these mixed-up squares in the spaces on the next page to put this picture back together. The letters and numbers tell you where each square belongs. The first one, A-3, has been done for you.

Illustrated by Rob Sepanak

	1	2	3	4
A			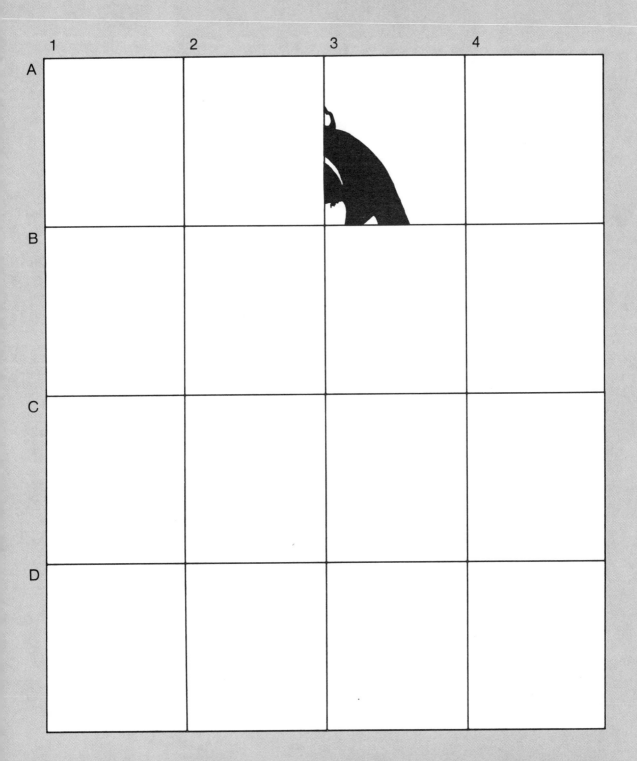	
B				
C				
D				

FINEST MINUS

Don't take anything away from this puzzle just because there are a lot of negatives to it. Subtraction symbols are hidden everywhere on this page. You'll be the finest if you can find every minus.

24

DOGS ON DISPLAY

Angela, Tiffany, Rodney, and Mike each had a dog that won an award in the city's annual dog show. The winning dogs were a poodle, a beagle, a bulldog, and a sheepdog. The awards were for Best Costume, Best Trick, Friendliest Dog, and Best in Show. Can you match each person with his or her dog and the dog's award?

1. The bulldog won the Friendliest Dog award, but Angela's dog didn't.
2. Rodney's dog won the Best Trick award, but the sheepdog didn't.
3. The sheepdog did not win the Best Costume award, but Tiffany's dog did.
4. The poodle couldn't do any tricks.

OWNER	DOG	AWARD
_____	_____	_____
_____	_____	_____
_____	_____	_____
_____	_____	_____

Illustrated by John Nez

Answer on page 49.

PAN-TASTIC

A kitchenful of pans are scattered throughout this puzzle. These pans appear where the letters PAN should go in certain words. As you are solving this puzzle, draw in each pan when you find it. Two words have been done as an example. Hint: PAN does not appear in every word.

ACROSS:

1. A sudden fear
3. Evil things came from ____'s box
7. Fast foward (abbreviation)
8. Glass container
9. Strong farm animal
10. Flesh around teeth
11. To look at
12. Seaport on the Black Sea
14. Short for "Susan"
15. Club knocked down in bowling
18. Opposite of winner
20. Color of apples and stop signs
22. Ending for "fool" or "baby"
23. Elevated railway (short form)
24. Small plant of violet family
25. To breathe fast; gasp
26. Metal bolt
27. To grow old

DOWN:

1. To cook in a skillet
2. In case that
3. Central American canal country
4. Doctor (abbreviation)
5. Fish eggs
6. Hatchets
8. Plant fiber used in burlap
10. Stuck together
11. The language of Spain
13. Abbreviation for American Samoa
15. Small flower or poem
16. Northeast (abbreviation)
17. Brother (form used in the South), as with Rabbit
18. To write words in order
19. Speed of movement
21. Boy's name
24. Section of a window
25. A sudden pain

Answer on page 49.

SKI-DADDLE

Charlotte was excited to be on her first ski trip of the season. Her brother took some photos of the day, but they are out of order. Can you number these pictures to show what happened first, second, and so on?

Illustrated by Jon Davis

Answer on page 49.

CAR SHOW MEMORIES

Take a long look at this picture. Try to remember everything you see in it. Then turn the page, and try to answer some questions about it without looking back.

Illustrated by Judith Hunt

DON'T READ THIS UNTIL YOU HAVE LOOKED AT "Car Show Memories" ON PAGE 29.

CAR SHOW MEMORIES   Part 2

Can you answer these questions about the car show scene you saw? Don't peek!

1. What was the name of the car on the front display?
2. What color was the car's display platform?
3. How much did the car cost?
4. How many balloons were tied to the back bumper?
5. Was the trunk open or closed on the display car?
6. What symbol was on the side of this car?
7. What letter had wings on someone's shirt?
8. What day of the week was it?
9. What kind of car was on display in the rear?
10. What symbol was on the side of the rear car?

Answer on page 49.

SOUND SENSE

What do each of these things have in common?

1.

3.

5.

2.

4.

6.

Illustrated by John Nez

Answer on page 49.

DOT MAGIC

A taxi from the Orient is waiting on this page. Draw a line connecting the dots before it takes off without you.

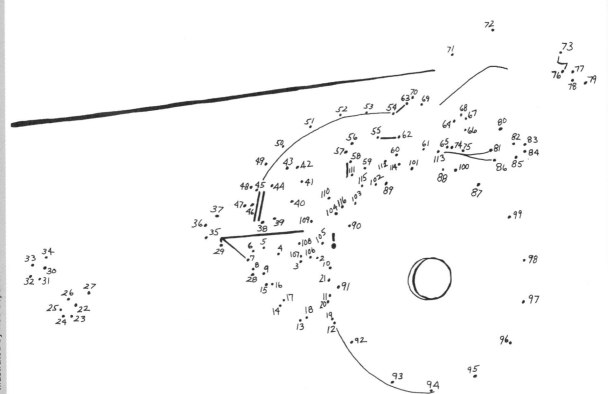

RIDDLE A-ROUND

The answers to two riddles are contained in the spiral on the next page.

For the answer to the first riddle, you will have to go to the center to the red O, and go counterclockwise, copying down every other letter onto the lines below riddle number one.

For the answer to the second riddle, start at the top with the red T. Go clockwise around the circle and copy down every other letter onto the blank lines below riddle number two. Go slowly and don't get dizzy!

1. What is the difference between a bus driver and a bad cold?

_____

_____

Answer on page 49.

2. What happened when it rained quarters, dimes, nickels, and pennies?

_____

_____

_____

PICTURE POSTCARDS

Rebus Rita has collected postcards from six of the 50 United States. Can you tell which ones?

Answer on page 49.

Illustrated by Gregg Valley

HERE'S AN EARFUL

Lend an ear and you'll discover that many words contain the letters EAR. Use these clues to find some words these letters appear in.

1. One of these is usually 365 days long: ___ ear

2. One fruit that sounds like two: ___ ear

3. Make your own money: ear ___

4. Not cloudy: ___ ___ ear

5. This planet: Ear ___ ___

6. Not late: ear ___ ___

7. Gain knowledge about something: ___ ear ___

8. Valentine symbol: ___ ear ___

9. Piece of jewelry: ear ___ ___ ___ ___

10. Completely brave: ___ ear ___ ___ ___ ___

11. One of these might fall when you're sad: ___ ear ___ ___ ___ ___

12. Vanish: ___ ___ ___ ___ ___ ___ ear

13. What goes on before your clothes: ___ ___ ___ ___ ___ ___ ear

14. Charming or loving: ___ ___ ___ ear ___ ___ ___

HIDDEN PICTURES

There are at least 35 objects hidden
in this scene. How many can you find?

Illustrated by Kit Wray

ARMS STRUGGLE

Oops! Orville, Oscar, Olivia and Bob were arm wrestling when things got out of hand. Can you unravel this mess, by figuring out which octopus is connected to which tentacle?

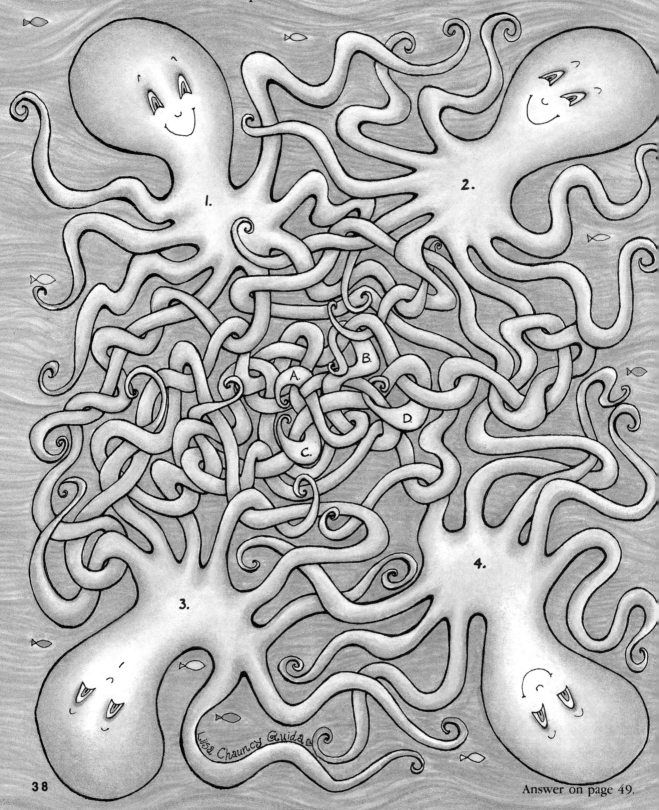

Answer on page 49.

SLIDE SHOW

Doctor Karloff has been examing all sorts of things under his microscope. Was he looking at a giant germ or a shrunken worm? A miniature car or a piece of candy bar? Use your imagination to draw in what's on the slide under this microscope.

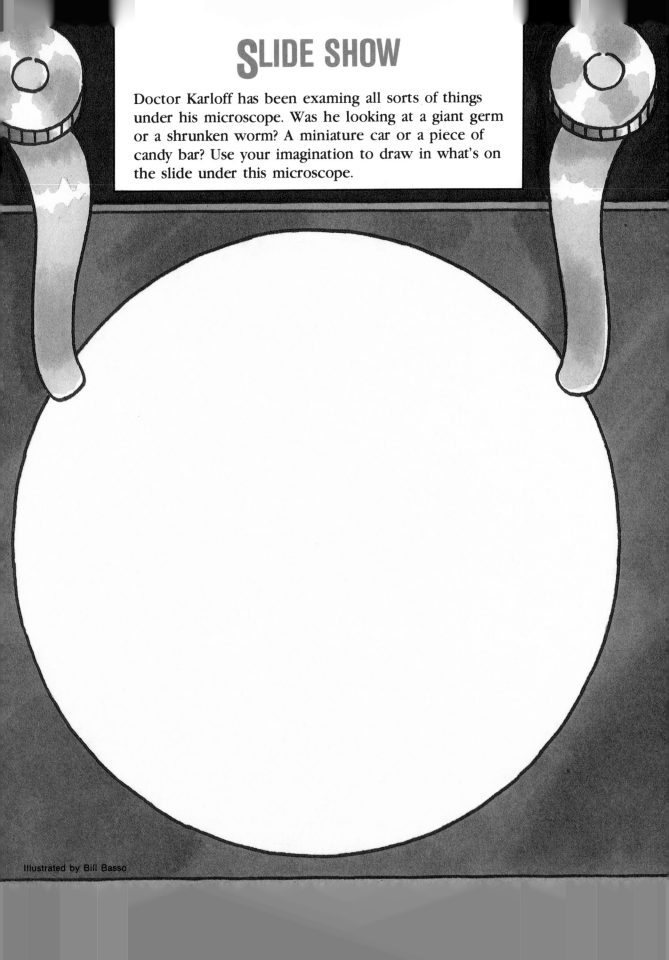

Illustrated by Bill Basso

BINARY BAFFLER

This cranky computer is acting up again! All but two of the buttons are stuck. However, the computer has come up with a code that uses only these two buttons to print out the message it wants to share. Use the key to crack the code and find out what's so funny.

A	=	3	O	=	3333
B	=	4	P	=	4444
C	=	33	Q	=	3334
D	=	44	R	=	3343
E	=	34	S	=	3433
F	=	43	T	=	3443
G	=	333	U	=	3444
H	=	444	V	=	4443
I	=	334	W	=	4333
J	=	343	X	=	4343
K	=	344	Y	=	4334
L	=	433	Z	=	4433
M	=	434	•	=	44443
N	=	443	?	=	33334

Illustrated by Tim Ellis

4333-444-3-3443   3-443-334-434-3-433

_____   _____

344-34-34-4444-3433   3443-444-34

_____   _____

4-34-3433-3443   3443-334-434-34-33334

_____   _____

3   4333-3-3443-33-444-44-3333-333-44443

_   _____

Answer on page 49.

MARVELOUS MARIONETTES

How many differences can you find between these two pictures?

Illustrated by Paul Richer

WHAT'S IN A WORD?

Even the funniest looking caterpillar can turn into a beautiful butterfly. The letters in CATERPILLAR can also be turned into beautiful words, like CAT and RACE. Without spinning a cocoon, see how many words of three letters or more you can find in CATERPILLAR?

CATERPILLAR

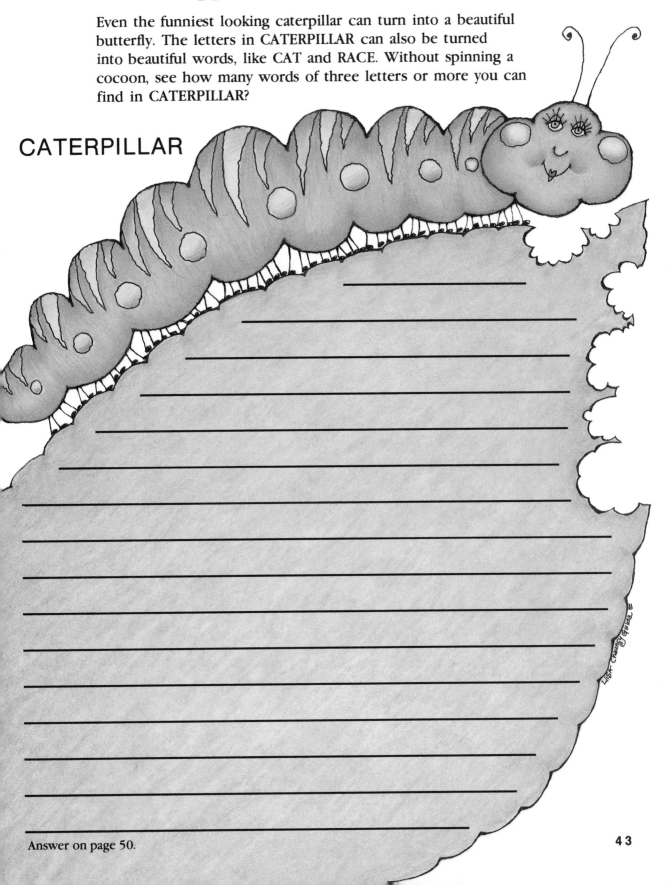

Answer on page 50.

DUMMY RUN

If Dominic doesn't deliver these dummies to the dress department, he'll be demoted. Can you help him find a path through this store to where his boss is waiting?

Answer on page 50.

BARNYARD BOO-BOOS

How many things can you find wrong in this picture?

ANSWERS

COVER

DOLL DILEMMA (page 3)

6 5 4 2 1 7 3

DAYS OF KNIGHTS (pages 4-5)

CHECK OUT THAT SHAPE (page 6)

FOREIGN PHRASES (page 7)

FAST FLOYD'S FLOWERS (pages 8-9)

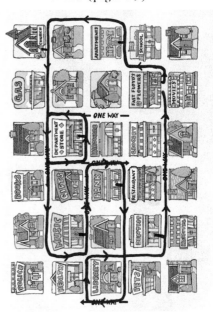

STRANGE SEQUENCES (page 10)
1. H letters of the alphabet
2. A (August) months of the year
3. S (Saturday) days of the week
4. I (indigo) colors in a rainbow
5. B the C Major musical scale
6. E (eight) counting numbers
7. P (Pluto) names of the planets
8. F (fourteen) even numbers

INSTANT PICTURE (page 11)

DEEP SLEEP (pages 12-13)
These animals and their vehicles are in the professor's dream:

Dragon Wagon	Shrimp Blimp
Sheep Jeep	Spider Glider
Crab Cab	Cow Plow
Collie Trolley	Bug Tug
Pig Rig	Frog Log
Duck Truck	Goat Boat
Crane Plane	Sardine Submarine

There are also two triple rhymes:

Maroon Raccoon Balloon
Blue Shrew Canoe

FISHING LINE (page 15)
Bookworms

ROME, SWEET ROME (pages 16-17)

ROW, ROW, ROW (page 18)

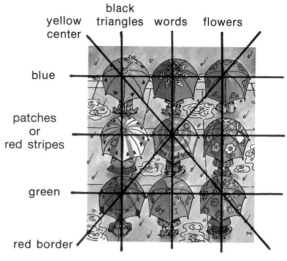

black
yellow   triangles   words   flowers
center

blue

patches
or
red stripes

green

red border

LUCKY LIST (page 19)
GOOD
four-leaf clover
wishbone
rabbit's foot
face-up penny
horseshoes
shooting star

BAD
stepping on sidewalk cracks
open umbrella inside
walk under ladder
cracked mirror
black cats
spilled salt

WEATHER WORRIES (pages 20-21)
1. Snow, in the 30s.
2. Cousin Vinnie in Oklahoma
3. It's icy.
4. Rain, in the 50s
5. From the 60s to the 90s
6. Thunderstorms, in the 80s
7. Southern California

PICTURE MIXER (pages 22-23)

DOGS ON DISPLAY (page 25)

Angela - sheepdog - Best in Show
Tiffany - poodle - Best Costume
Rodney - beagle - Best Trick
Mike - bulldog - Friendliest Dog

PAN-TASTIC (pages 26-27)

SKI-DADDLE (page 28)

CAR SHOW MEMORIES (page 30)

1. The Tiger X-5
2. Purple
3. $25,000
4. Four
5. Closed
6. Tiger's paw
7. A
8. Thursday
9. A van
10. Pegasus

SOUND SENSE (page 30)

Each picture can be represented by a single letter of the alphabet.

1 - B (Bee)
2 - C (Sea)
3 - I (Eye)
4 - J (Jay)
5 - P (Pea)
6 - T (Tea)

DOT MAGIC (page 31)

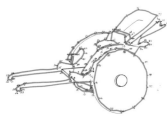

RIDDLE A-ROUND (pages 32-33)

1. One knows the stops, the other stops the nose.
2. There was quite a lot of change in the weather.

PICTURE POSTCARDS (page 34)

1. Colorado
2. Connecticut
3. North Carolina
4. Oregon
5. Washington
6. Minnesota

HERE'S AN EARFUL (page 35)

1. year
2. pear
3. earn
4. clear
5. Earth
6. early
7. learn
8. heart
9. earring
10. fearless
11. teardrop
12. disappear
13. underwear
14. endearing

ARMS STRUGGLE (page 38)

1. C
2. B
3. A
4. D

BINARY BAFFLER (pages 40-41)

WHAT'S IN A WORD? (page 43)

Here are the words we found. You may have found others.

ace	caper	eat	pail	place	rite
ail	car	ice	pair	plate	tail
air	care	ill	pale	pleat	tall
all	carp	irate	parcel	price	tarp
altar	cart	ire	pare	race	tear
alter	cater	lace	part	rail	tell
ape	cell	lap	pear	rate	tile
arc	cellar	lapel	pearl	real	till
are	clap	late	pier	recall	tire
art	clear	later	pile	relic	trace
ate	crate	lice	pill	retail	trail
call	ear	lip	pillar	rice	trap
cape	earl	pace	pirate	ripe	trial

DUMMY RUN (pages 44-45)

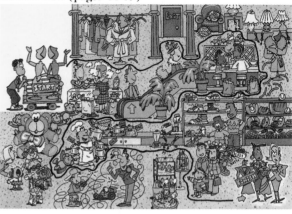

Editor: Jeffrey A. O'Hare • **Art Director:** Timothy J. Gillner
Project Director: Pamela Gallo • **Editorial Consultant:** Andrew Gutelle
Design Consultant: Bob Feldgus

Puzzle Contributors
Betty Lou Adamovich • Barbara Backer • James S. Dorr • Ann Fisher
Jeanette C. Grote • Isobel Livingstone • Karen Morrell • Patricia Talley